JOURNEY OF THE THIRTY GILT PENNIES

TRACE THEIR JOURNEY

FROM UR TO HEBRON AND CANAAN
FROM HEBRON TO EGYPT
FROM EGYPT TO SHEBA
FROM SHEBA TO JERUSALEM
FROM JERUSALEM TO BABYLON
FROM BABYLON TO BETHLEHEM
FROM BETHLEHEM TO JERUSALEM

TEHERAN
(IRAN)

A

INDIAN OCEAN

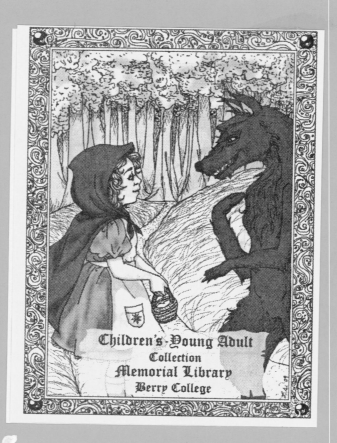

THE THIRTY GILT PENNIES

THE
THIRTY
GILT
PENNIES

ALICE GEER KELSEY

PICTURES BY GORDON LAITE

ABINGDON PRESS   NASHVILLE   NEW YORK

When You
Read a Legend

*R*emember that a legend is an old, old story which has pleased people so much they like to tell it to their children and their grandchildren. Those grandchildren tell it to their children and their grandchildren. From the beginning, the storytellers know they cannot prove the story and really have no desire to say, "This is exactly the way it happened." It is enough for lovers of legends if they can say, "This story shows how people felt about a man, a deed, or a country . . . or those shining gilt pennies."

The story of *The Thirty Gilt Pennies* has become a part of the legend of the three kings. But the pennies and their stories were very old long before the kings rode out of the East to bring gifts to the Christ child at Bethlehem. The legend of the pennies spreads from three thousand years before and some thirty years after the birth of Jesus. Legends have a way of spreading out in many directions.

9

The reader of the legend of *The Thirty Gilt Pennies* must not ask too many practical questions. He must not ask, "How does it happen that King Ninus was having coins made in 2000 B.C. when my coin collection book states that money was first minted by order of the King of Lydia, about 500 B.C.?" Fourteenth-century legend writers did not have encyclopedias for looking up facts. A few centuries, more or less, did not trouble them.

The reader may wonder, "How did those coins change from silver to gilt to gold without any magic wands waving over them?" John of Hildesheim explains that the three words—silver, gilt, and gold—were used in those days for any shiny metal mined from the earth.

Perhaps the reader will ask, "How did it happen that those thirty gilt pennies had different values at times in their story?" Legends are not history compiled by computers. Legends show only what seemed important to people at a given time.

Do not say, "I cannot believe thirty coins could stay together for over two thousand years, always popping up when needed for something special!" Perhaps not in history, but easily in a legend.

The legend of *The Thirty Gilt Pennies* is not offered as a substitute for the biblical stories from which the legend comes. Read the biblical stories for yourself.

Have you ever stood on a beach to skip stones on a smooth pond? The pebble makes only a splash and a ripple when it touches the surface, then bounds on to touch again and again, then sinks below the water. In the legend of *The Thirty Gilt Pennies* the underlying Bible story is like the smooth and unchanged surface of the water. The thirty gilt pennies are like the looping, splashing, bounding, rippling, skipping stones. Twelve times the coins touch the ongoing Bible story. After the twelfth skip, they disappear forever.

Forever? Who can know?

The Boy
Who Collected Legends

There lived in the walled city of Hildesheim, in Germany, in the fourteenth century a boy who collected legends. His name? Nobody really knows. Many years later historians and other writers referred to him as John of Hildesheim.

Life was not dull for a boy in Hildesheim. Life was especially good for a boy who collected legends. There was always something in the town or in the surrounding countryside for John and his friends to see, or hear, or do.

To the east the Innerste River invited them to swim, to fish, to skip stones, to study aquatic life, or launch toy boats. And they could stand on the river's banks to watch real boats sailing to the bigger Weser River that flowed into the North Sea.

To the south of Hildesheim rose the foothills of the wild and beautiful Harz Mountains, luring John and his friends to explore. In the wooded hills yellow-brown deer stepped quietly. Thistle finch chirped

in the beech trees, and squirrels scampered from branch to branch of tall fir trees. When the boys ventured into deeper woods where the very stillness provided excitement, they could share stories they had heard of lynx and bear lurking behind rocks and evergreens. Climbing higher, they could visit mountain mines that produced metal for the famous craftsmen of Hildesheim.

John probably took turns herding sheep and cattle in the pasture land between city walls and foothills of the Harz Mountains. Nowhere else, it was said, did sheep bells tinkle so sweetly or cattle bells peal so clearly. These made melodious background for a boy's thoughts. But in John's opinion no sound could compare with the voice of a storyteller.

"Tell me the story," John would urge when anyone even hinted at a legend concerning a person, a place, or an event unknown to John.

"Is there a story about it?" John would ask when he stopped to watch the metal craftsmen as their hammers tapped merrily.

"Always he wants the story," some of the workmen would answer and go right on with their steady rat-a-tat. Others saw John's eager eyes and took time to tell him the legend of the statue or the engraving which was taking form under their skilled touch.

Fourteenth-century Germany rang with music and drama. There were skilled programs of the Meistersinger, mystery plays based on Bible stories, festivals, cathedral choirs, and folk singing. There was singing in the marketplace, in homes, in the cathedral and churches, and on the town green. Always John listened for the stories in the music.

We can imagine John drinking in every word sung by highway minstrels. If the ballad ended too soon, he might ask, "What happened next?" Some singers simply started another song, but some caught the excitement in John's voice and rested their fiddles or cymbals while they told him what they knew of the heroes or heroines of their songs.

The great cathedral of Hildesheim was a wonderful place for John's "Tell me the story about it." He had asked so often about the two heavy bronze doors with their series of pictures that he knew perfectly the Bible story of Adam portrayed on one door and the stories of Jesus Christ etched on the other. There were still more pictures of the life of Jesus on a towering bronze column. A white-cloaked Carmelite friar told the boy how the column had been molded three hundred years before and brought to the cathedral of Hildesheim.

John had heard over and over again the stories about Saint Bernward, the bishop, whose love of beauty had been responsible for the doors and the column. He had heard stories of the saints whose tombs were in the cathedral—Saint Godehard, Saint Epiphanius, and others. All these stories John knew; but in the cathedral there was something else. This provided a tale so strange that John never tired of hearing it.

"Where did those come from?" John would ask, pointing to a case containing three bony fingers. The friar or the teacher would smile and begin again the story John knew very well:

"You have heard about the three kings who rode out of the East to bring gifts to the Christ child at Bethlehem?"

"I know their story," John would admit.

"These fingers are from the blessed hands that carried those gifts of gold, frankincense, and myrrh to the Christ child." The answer was always the same, though some of the speakers might go so far as to point out which finger was Melchior's, which was Balthazar's, and which was Gaspar's.

"How did the fingers come here? Hildesheim is far from Bethlehem. Hildesheim is even farther from the homes of the three kings of the East." John knew what the answer would be, but it was all so strange. Perhaps some words in a new telling would explain it. "Tell me, please," he would ask again.

"Many years ago Rainald of Dassel was Archbishop of Cologne," the answer usually began. "In the year 1164 the archbishop visited Milan, a city in Italy. There he found something he wanted to bring back to Germany. The archbishop was a determined man. When he left Milan, he took with him a new treasure for the great cathedral of Cologne."

"What was it?" John asked, though of course he already knew.

"Three big boxes," was the answer. "In each box was the body of one of the three kings who crossed the eastern deserts to worship the child king at Bethlehem, more than eleven hundred years before the archbishop made his visit to Milan."

"How did Rainald know 'twas the three kings in the three boxes?" John wanted to know. "And how did the boxes get to Italy?"

"There were many legends—old, old stories about the three kings," the friar would begin, and John listened carefully, hoping to learn something new. "These legends told how each of the three kings learned from his own astrologers about the new star and its prophecy—."

If the storyteller paused for breath, John would urge him on. "What else?" John would ask.

"The legends tell how each king decided what to take as his gift for the new king. And there are stories of how they met together for the first time outside the gates of Jerusalem. You know how they journeyed together to the humble stable in Bethlehem," the patient priest or friar would go on. "You know how the three kings worshiped the Christ child, how they hurried to escape the suspicious King Herod, and how they traveled throughout the East, telling of the child who would become a great king. According to the legends the three kings talked about the Christ child until their death. Another story tells how the graves of the kings were found by a pious queen named Helena. All these stories and others came out of the East at the time the coffins of the three sainted kings were brought to the cathedral in Milan."

"But these fingers!" John would interrupt. "How did they get to Hildesheim?"

"Though Rainald was Archbishop of Cologne, he was not too proud to remember his student days in Hildesheim. He wanted to do something for the town where he had studied. And so he shared with Hildesheim the greatest treasure of the cathedral of Cologne. He could not send us the bodies of the three kings, but he gave us a finger of each."

As John grew up in Hildesheim, he heard new legends of the three kings from pilgrims who came to see the fingers. These were legends of the three kings in their own countries before they had seen the star that led them to Bethlehem. And stories about what happened to the kings after they had presented their gifts to the Christ child and departed, each for his own country.

23

During John's growing years, he probably made a pilgrimage with his family to the cathedral of Cologne. Viewing with wonder the caskets of the three kings, John did not need to ask why each lacked one finger. The pilgrimages might have been on Epiphany or Three Kings' Day, twelve days after Christmas. Archbishop Rainald had decreed that the sum of ten marks yearly be used for the three kings' festival on that day. Pilgrims from far and near came for these celebrations. In those days of the fourteenth century, legendary heroes were popular with everyone, not only with story-hungry boys like John of Hildesheim. The ever-listening boy could add more bits to the storehouse of legends in his memory.

Growing up to love the churches and cathedrals of Hildesheim, John chose to join the order of Carmelite friars. Dressed in white cloak over brown habit, he kept his vows faithfully—praying, studying, teaching, working, begging. There were Latin, Greek, and German scrolls in the Carmelite library. Friar John had not lost his boyish fondness for stories, especially for stories about the three kings.

Imagine his delight when he read in one of the scrolls in the monastery a legend that was new to him—a legend which included his beloved three kings. This one had been written by Godfrey of Viterbo, who was born about 1120, probably in Italy. Godfrey went from Italy to Germany and became secretary to King Frederick I, known as Frederick Barbarossa (Red Beard). King Frederick made many journeys throughout his realm and into neighboring lands. His secretary traveled with him. Godfrey had a good ear for history and legend, and he wrote about what he heard.

He was traveling and writing at the time the bodies of the three kings were carried in their boxes from Milan to Cologne. With the removal of the bodies there was a fresh spurt of the telling of the legends of the kings. Then Godfrey heard and wrote an account of an

unfamiliar legend. Years later, John found it in the library of the Carmelite monastery.

Godfrey's story was about the gold that Melchior gave to the Christ child at Bethlehem. John liked this new legend that wove the story of Melchior's gold into Bible stories going back three thousand years. John was both student and teacher of the Bible now. He knew all these Bible stories well. It pleased him to associate the legends of the three kings with such biblical heroes as Abraham, Jacob, Joseph, and Solomon. The story of thirty shining coins was added to John's treasury of legends.

At last, during the quiet hours in the Carmelite monastery, John of Hildesheim had time to put in writing the legends he had collected since the days of his childhood. John cherished the stories and wanted to believe every word of them. He did not examine them carefully to be sure all their facts were true. He did, however, have a test for all the legends. They must be true to the character of the three kings who dared start out across hill and desert, led only by a new and glorious star. For his written collection, John of Hildesheim chose legends that showed the kings as wise, generous, brave, and full of faith.

Written in Latin, John of Hildesheim's HISTORIA TRIUM REGNUM (STORY OF THE THREE KINGS) tells the legend of these wise men of the East as John pieced the story together from mystery plays, histories, religious books, and from tales of pilgrims who came to Hildesheim or Cologne. John's book became famous and was translated from Latin into other languages. One of these was English so old and quaint that it is hard to recognize it as our own language:

Fferthemore ye schul vndirstonde, as hit
is aforseyde, that Melchior, kyng of
Nubye and of arabie, offrid to godd a
rounde appil of gold and .xxx gilt
penyes. of thes .xxx gilt penyes ye
schul here the first bygynnyng and the
last ende.

27

The
Thirty Gilt Pennies

*T*erah the metal craftsman never dreamed of being noticed by
the great King Ninus of Ur in Babylonia. Often Terah passed
the palace walls on his way to the marketplace, or to the courtyard of
the great temple of the moon-god to sell his handiwork: copper dishes,
silver ornaments, or golden statuettes. Terah no more expected King
Ninus to speak to him than he expected the moon-god to float down
from the skies for a leisurely chat.

Terah and his three sons, Abraham, Nahor, and Haran, were solid
citizens of Ur. They were respected by their neighbors who were fisher-
men, farmers, merchants, or craftsmen. Terah's family lived in a good
house of baked clay brick. They had flocks and herds grazing in the
lush pasturelands of the Euphrates River valley. They owned irrigated
vineyards that supplied them with grapes, figs, dates, and olives.

One day the unexpected happened. A courier came from great King
Ninus with a message for Terah. "The king wants his name and his

picture engraved on golden discs. Follow me to the king's palace. He will tell you exactly what you must do."

Astonished, Terah went to the palace. His three sons watched him go. They were proud that King Ninus had chosen their father as the master metal craftsman of Ur.

Terah listened well. He did all the king ordered. He used finest gold, brought by traders' caravans from Arabia where the best gold was mined. With great care and skill he fashioned the molds engraved with the face and name of King Ninus. Terah's golden discs were shining and beautiful. Any craftsman could be proud of them.

The king was pleased. "Terah," said the king, "your work is excellent. You have done a fine job. As payment you shall have—what will it be?"

Terah ventured no answer, and King Ninus said, "I know the proper payment." He counted out thirty of the gold coins. "You must have thirty of these gilt pennies. These shall be yours."

His sons were surprised when Terah repeated to them the words of the king.

"No sheep?" the sons asked. "No cattle? No great treasure for the king's master craftsman? Only these? What can you do with them?"

"These," Terah said, "are made of the finest gold. They will last forever. They shall belong to me and to my sons, and to the sons of my sons, for as long as we are on earth." And Terah placed the round gold pieces in a treasure chest.

The years passed.

Terah's son Abraham grew into a strong young man. He thought for himself and was never afraid to question the customs of his day. He did not like what he saw at the temple of the moon-god.

"I do not believe in the moon-god our neighbors worship," Abraham told his father. "Let us leave these people and journey to a new land where we can be free of this false worship. I am sure there is a greater God than the moon-god. In a new land we could think and worship as we please. We could find the true God—and worship him."

It took much courage to leave their comfortable home in Ur, but Abraham talked long and well. "My wife Sarah and I are going anyway. Do come with us."

Finally Terah agreed to go with Abraham. With them also went Abraham's nephew Lot, the son of Haran. They packed what they could carry, including the treasure chest containing the thirty gilt pennies. They made a long caravan—the family riding on donkeys, followed by servants, herdsmen, and flocks, and pack donkeys loaded with goods.

Slowly Terah's caravan followed the fertile valley of the Euphrates River, stopping while donkeys and flocks drank, grazed, or rested. In villages along the way, Terah's family traded for the things they needed. They could exchange goats' milk cheese for a basket of figs, a young donkey for a jar of cooking oil, sheeps' wool for a basket of nuts, a lamb for a bag of grain. Always the thirty gilt pennies stayed in the treasure chest, the prized heirloom to be passed on to Terah's gandchildren.

At last they settled in Mesopotamia. There they stayed until Terah died, a very old man.

After leaving Ur, Abraham had begun to know the God who was far greater than the moon-god of Ur. Now this great God urged Abraham to leave this fertile valley between the Tigris and Euphrates

Rivers—to move again to a new land. Abraham had great faith in the God he was learning to know. With his family and helpers, he traveled on to the land of Canaan.

Again they depended on milk and wool from their flocks. They traded sheep, cattle, or goats for anything they might need. Carefully, Abraham kept together the thirty gilt pennies that had been given to his father by King Ninus of Ur. Even if Abraham had wished to spend these treasures, the people with whom he traded preferred a plump goat to a bit of shiny metal, no matter how perfectly the face of King Ninus was engraved upon it.

Abraham found good pasture for his flocks in the land of Canaan. He did not build houses of clay brick like those left behind in Ur. He was no longer a city dweller, though there were cities in the land. Living away from the cities, he had time to know better the God he had left Ur to find. Abraham and his people chose to live in tents that could be moved with their flocks to hills, plains, or valleys as the seasons changed—high up in the hills in summer, down into the warm valleys in winter.

Abraham's flocks increased. His family increased. Abraham reached old age, healthy through outdoor living, wise through meditation and prayer.

And then Abraham's beloved wife Sarah died. For her Abraham must have a burial cave that would belong to him and his sons forever. Nomadic shepherds and herdsmen do not own fields or hillsides with caves in them. Abraham had lived wherever the pasture was good, and now he had no piece of land to call his own, no cave where he could lay Sarah's body.

Abraham went to the Hittites, the people who owned the land where

he pitched his tents. He found them gathered in their favorite talking place, the open square at the gate of their walled town.

"I am a stranger among you," Abraham told them. "I own no land. May I have a place of my own to bury my good wife Sarah?"

Politely the Hittites answered, "You are a mighty prince. Bury your dead in the choicest of our tombs. None of us will hold back his cave, nor hinder you from burying your dead."

Abraham bowed with great courtesy and answered, "Ask Ephron the son of Zohar to give me the cave of Machpelah which he owns. It is at the end of his field. For the full price let him give it to me in your presence. Let it be mine for a burying place."

Ephron spoke so all the Hittites sitting about the gate could hear him. "I give you the field. I give you the cave that is in it. In the presence of the sons of my people, I give it to you. Bury your dead."

Abraham was proud. He bowed deeply again to Ephron and said, "I will give the price of the field. Accept it from me that I may bury my dead."

Ephron chose a polite way of sounding generous while letting Abraham know how much to pay. "My lord," said Ephron, "listen to me. A piece of land worth four hundred shekels of silver, what is that between you and me? Bury your dead."

Abraham could not permit Sarah's body to lie in a field or cave which did not belong to him. And so to Ephron Abraham gave the thirty golden coins, the thirty gilt pennies on which his father so long ago had engraved the picture and the name of King Ninus. The treasure had gone from Terah's family.

The years passed.

In Canaan there lived a man named Jacob, who was the grandson of Abraham. Jacob had many sons, but Joseph was his favorite. Joseph received far more attention from his father than did his older brothers. And Joseph had the poor sense to repeat his marvelous dreams to them —dreams in which Joseph was always better and more important than his brothers.

One day while the ten shepherd brothers were herding their flocks, they saw Joseph walking across the fields toward them. It was bad enough that he was free to wander about while they worked, but today they saw something that made them even more jealous. Their pampered younger brother was dressed in the latest gift from their father—a long-sleeved coat of many colors, much finer than the rough working clothes the older brothers always wore.

"Here comes that boy!" muttered the brothers. "He's probably coming to tell us his latest dream."

Their patience with Joseph had reached an end. They plotted to get rid of him—now, when their father was not nearby to stand up for him. It was easy for ten strong shepherds to overpower the younger boy. They threw him into a deep pit.

"What shall we do with him now?" was their new problem. They had many ideas but could not agree. While they were arguing, a caravan of Ishmaelite traders came along.

"Would you like to buy a strong young slave?" the brothers asked as the traders drew near.

The traders looked Joseph over carefully. They offered only a low price because he was young and because he did not look as though he was used to hard labor. Apparently the Ishmaelites had been trading in the part of Hebron where Ephron the Hittite once had lived. The traders had in their possession some unusual coins.

"Look," said one of the traders. "Perhaps you would like as payment these most unusual coins. No doubt they are of great value."

The bargain was made. The thirty gilt pennies were paid for a young slave who was carried off to be sold again in Egypt.

Jacob wept, thinking Joseph had been killed, and would not be comforted. Joseph's older brothers dared not tell their father the truth, and the thirty gilt pennies were kept hidden for a long, long time.

Years passed.

A time came when there was a great famine in Canaan. Travelers reported there was grain for sale in Egypt. So down to Egypt went the sons of Jacob, carrying gold to trade for grain. This, they thought, would be a good time to spend those thirty gilt pennies they had been hiding.

Arriving in Egypt the sons of Jacob had to deal with a handsome young man who was in charge of the king's granaries. They did not recognize him as their younger brother Joseph whom they had sold to the traders many years before. But Joseph recognized them. Not knowing that he understood their language, the brothers talked freely in front of him. Listening, he learned they were loyal sons of Jacob. He even learned they were sorry for the grief they had caused their father when they sold their younger brother.

The brothers paid for the grain and started their journey north. Reaching home, they found in their bags of grain the money they had given in payment. Once more the thirty gilt pennies were in their possession to haunt and disturb them. The brothers were confused and worried.

Later they were even more distressed. The grain they had brought from Egypt was eaten, but the famine in Canaan continued. It was necessary to go back to Egypt. Once more they carried the thirty gilt pennies.

Again they did not recognize Joseph. Again their purchase money, including the thirty gilt pennies, was slipped into their bags of grain. This time Joseph sent a servant running after them to call them back to him. Fearfully, they returned. What would happen if they were accused of stealing?

Joseph was forgiving. "I am your brother," he told them. "Go. Bring our father and all your families to Egypt."

So Jacob and his sons and grandchildren were together at last in Egypt. And the thirty gilt pennies were finished with traveling for awhile.

Years passed.

Jacob, the father of Joseph, grew old and died. His sons had learned from the Egyptians about embalming the dead. They wished to use the choicest spices to embalm their honored father.

"Where do we find the best spices?" they asked of their Egyptian neighbors.

The answer was always the same: "From the land of Sheba."

Into the marketplace went the sons of Jacob to buy spices brought by merchants across the Arabian desert from the land of Sheba, that triangle of land between the Red Sea and the Gulf of Aden. The land

of Sheba was said to be a fabulous country, watered by irrigation ditches to make it fertile for growing many kinds of spices.

By the time the brothers located merchants from the land of Sheba, they were ready to pay any price for the proper spices. The cost was great, and when the bargaining had finished, the thirty gilt pennies had changed hands again.

The sons of Jacob carried their father's embalmed body back to the land of Canaan. They buried it in the family's cave in the field of Machpelah—the same cave their great-grandfather Abraham had bought as a burial place for his beloved Sarah, and for which he had paid the thirty gilt pennies made by Terah of Ur.

Centuries passed.

In the ninth century B.C. Sheba was ruled by a mighty queen who was as clever and strong-minded as she was wealthy. She was proud of her country, fragrant with its fields and orchards of world-famous spices. There was only one problem. In Jerusalem, 1,250 miles to the northeast by camel route, there ruled a king named Solomon. Merchants and other travelers brought to Sheba fabulous tales of Solomon's wealth, his wisdom, his power—and the growing boundaries of his kingdom. The queen of Sheba heard of Solomon's trade agreements with King Hiram of Tyre and other rulers.

"The caravans from my land must travel through territory ruled by Solomon," said the shrewd queen of Sheba. "My country, like Tyre, should have trade agreements with a king who is so wealthy and so strong. It is far better to have friends than enemies as neighbors."

Some queens might have sent trusted couriers on a diplomatic mission to the mighty king in Jerusalem. But the queen of Sheba said, "I must see for myself if the rich King Solomon is really as all-knowing and all-powerful as he is said to be."

There was hustle and bustle in the land of Sheba as its queen made ready her caravan for the journey to Jerusalem. Some camels carried gifts of spices, precious stones, and gold for King Solomon. Other camels carried the queen's traveling companions and attendants. The queen herself rode in a canopied seat on the finest camel of all.

Arriving in Jerusalem, the queen was even more impressed than she had expected to be. She asked many questions, even tricky riddles. Solomon answered all with great wisdom. Many gifts were exchanged, and Solomon promised protection for spice caravans traveling north from the land of Sheba.

King Solomon was much too rich to need all the gold and jewels given him by the queen of Sheba. And he scarcely noticed at all a small chest containing thirty gilt pennies.

Centuries passed.

The nineteenth king after Solomon the Great was Jehoiachin, who was only eighteen years old when he came to the throne. A likable young man, Jehoiachin never had a chance to prove he could be a good ruler of Judah. His father King Jehoiakim had died, leaving the kingdom in hopeless confusion and danger. The powerful Babylonian armies led by King Nebuchadnezzar were marching toward Jerusalem. Jehoiachin had no armies strong enough to defend his kingdom or his great walled city Jerusalem.

Only three months and ten days after Jehoiachin took his throne, he surrendered to King Nebuchadnezzar. The young king, with Queen Mother Nehushta and some ten thousand Jews, was carried into captivity in Babylon. The exiles included the most useful citizens of the land: soldiers, craftsmen, smiths, royal princes, officials, and servants of the palace. Only the poorest and most helpless persons were left in their homeland.

King Nebuchadnezzar's men searched Jerusalem for treasure to take to Babylon. They found it in homes and in marketplaces. They found the greatest treasures in the temple built by Solomon. For more than three centuries the temple treasury had been enriched by gifts from loyal subjects and visiting kings. Among these treasures was the small chest, holding the thirty gilt pennies brought by the queen of Sheba to win the friendship of Solomon.

So, out of the temple treasury, the thirty gilt pennies went back across the wide desert to Babylon into the fertile valley of the Euphrates River. Now they were back within a few miles of Ur, where they had been minted by Terah for King Ninus.

After years of exile in Babylon, Jews began to return to their homeland. They rebuilt their walled city and the temple. But the treasures which Nebuchadnezzar's men had taken from the temple stayed in the East. No doubt the thirty gilt pennies were traded many times—perhaps again for a slave or an assortment of fabulous spices, or perhaps they were presented as a gift to a neighbor king.

Centuries passed.

King Melchior, ruler of Arabia and Nubia, was planning a long journey across the desert to the small country of Judea, home of the Jews. Judea was no longer a proud kingdom as in the days of King Solomon. Conquered by one country after another, little Judea was now ruled by the all-powerful Roman Empire. But strange news had to come to Melchior of a new king in Judea. The trip to Judea would be a tiring one, a long distance by camelback, but Melchior felt he must go. It was necessary for one king to greet another. But this new king was unknown. King Melchior had heard of him from his astrologers, men who studied the stars and read old prophecies. The astrologers had discovered a new star, blazing in the heavens, such as one mentioned in old, old prophecies:

> *A star shall arise out of Jacob*
> *and a man shall arise in Israel,*
> *And he shall rule all people.*

The astrologers were excited about the tremendous new star and about the prophecy of the ruler. Caught up in their excitement, King Melchior hurried to prepare for the journey to greet the new king.

"What gift shall I take him?" Melchior wondered. When one king visited another, he always carried gifts. Gold seemed the natural thing to take from Arabia and Nubia, kingdoms where the finest gold of the world was mined. King Melchior filled his camels' saddlebags with gold in many shapes, incuding a golden apple which had come from Alexander the Great, King of Macedonia. He chose also thirty quaint coins engraved with the face and name of an ancient king. Melchior did not recognize the king's name, but quite obviously the coins were of good Arabian gold. Perhaps they would be the very thing to intrigue a new king.

King Melchior and his caravan started across the lonely desert. He did not know his destination, but he followed the brilliant new star which shone each night in the western sky. Men and camels rested by day. Night by night, Melchior's caravan followed the star, first by camel trail and finally by a broad road going northwest.

Within sight of the high walls of the great city of Jerusalem, that road joined two other roads leading into the city. But clouds hid the star which guided the caravan. Melchior and his servants waited for the clouds to pass, and as they waited, a royal caravan approached on each of the other roads. They met where Melchior's caravan rested. The three kings soon found they were on the same mission—to meet a new king whose coming had been foretold by the astrologers in their three countries. The star had led them all to this spot. When the clouds had lifted, the three caravans went together into Jerusalem.

"Where is he who has been born king of the Jews?" they asked of those they met. "We have seen his star in the East and have come to worship him."

When the question reached the ears of King Herod of Judea, Herod was not pleased. If these three kings of the East had rumors of someone who might take his throne, King Herod wanted all the facts.

Herod had good reason to know the Jews had little love for him. They would welcome the idea of a new king. He called together the learned men of the temple and of his court. Herod was frightened and angered by the scholars' words: "It is written by the prophet that a new ruler will come from Bethlehem."

And you, O Bethlehem, in the land of Judah,
are by no means least among the rulers of Judah;
for from you shall come a ruler
who will govern my people Israel.

Herod reported this to the three kings. Then, hiding his real purpose for finding the newborn king, Herod told the three, "Go and search diligently, and when you have found him, bring me the word that I too may come and worship him."

Under a clear night sky the three kings followed the star toward the nearby town of Bethlehem. Crossing hilly pastures, they stopped to speak to shepherds who told strange tales of a wonderful baby born in a Bethlehem stable. It was, said the shepherds, lowly even among stables. It was the enclosure where animals were kept on their way to be sold in the marketplace. The three kings could not believe a stable would be the birthplace of a king they had traveled hundreds of miles to honor. They rode on, following the star and wondering.

At last the star seemed to stand still—and over a stable. The shepherds were right. The place had not even a whisper of royalty about it.

At the same moment the three kings had almost the same thought. Was this the king for whom each of them had brought a bag full of rich gifts? Looking at the simple clothes and humble bearing of the young mother and her carpenter husband, they thought their expensive gifts seemed out of place. But they must give something. Each king reached into his bag and pulled out the first article he touched. With low bows and words of reverence, each presented what he had taken from his bag. Gaspar gave myrrh. Balthazar gave frankincense. Melchior gave the golden apple and the thirty gilt pennies. The three kings knelt before the child while Mary and Joseph thanked them and wondered what this worship of their baby could mean.

When the three kings had left on their long journeys to their own kingdoms, Mary and Joseph talked together about the strange visit, about the unexpected gifts, and about their own plans for the wonderful baby who had been trusted to their care.

A warning of danger came to Joseph in a dream. "Rise!" warned the dream angel. "Take the young child and his mother. Flee to Egypt for safety. King Herod has heard that your baby will someday be king. Herod does not plan to let that happen. He is searching for the child to kill him."

"Mary! Mary!" Joseph awakened his sleeping wife. "I have had a dream we must obey." He repeated the warning of the dream angel.

Mary was excited and flurried. She took great care of the precious newborn baby, and in the few moments left she made the gifts from the three kings ready for the trip. They were wrapped in a cloth and the bundle tucked in the donkey's saddlebags.

It was a long journey from Bethlehem to Egypt—two hundred miles or more by jogging donkey. Somehow, somewhere along the way the gifts were lost. Perhaps their weight wore a hole in the saddlebags, and the bundle of gifts slipped through. Perhaps someone took them while Mary and Joseph slept by the roadside.

A shepherd, tending his flocks, found the cloth-wrapped treasures. It was a great and unexpected find. He had no way of locating the owner, so the treasure became the shepherd's. His wife and his children enjoyed the fragrance of the myrrh and frankincense, but he carefully hoarded the thirty gilt pennies.

Years passed.

The shepherd who had found the treasure supported his wife and family by his flocks and herds. He had no need of the coins for buying anything. His neighbors would always take his wool and his cheese or his mutton, in exchange for grain or corn. But the shepherd liked to look at the thirty gilt pennies, so pretty and so shiny. For thirty years he treasured them.

And then sickness struck the shepherd. Very ill, he consulted doctors of his land. Though he paid them well in sheep or goats or wool, the doctors could not cure him.

There came a day when the shepherd heard wonderful news. A traveler from the north said, "In the land of Judea there is a great teacher and healer. He has cured people of many different diseases. Even lepers have been made clean by him."

Sick as he was, the shepherd traveled north. Now he knew why he had saved the thirty gilt pennies all those years. Wrapped in their cloth and tied in the moneybag that dangled from his waist, they were much easier for the sick shepherd to carry than sheep or goats. *Surely this new healer would ask a great price*—the shepherd patted the moneybag containing the treasure and hurried on.

As he traveled, he heard more of the healer. Many persons he met on the road mentioned the carpenter from Nazareth, the healer who was causing such a stir in the Jewish land ruled by the Romans. The shepherd learned that the healer's name was Jesus and that he had gone to Jerusalem. The shepherd hurried on.

The city of Jerusalem was crowded with people who had come to celebrate the Feast of the Passover. There was great excitement in Jerusalm and its neighboring towns. The shepherd had no trouble finding people to help him locate the man from Nazareth. At last he saw a milling crowd surrounding a tall man with a face of merciful kindness.

Some men were praising him; others were cursing him. Some men were listening to his every word; others were talking among themselves. Some were carrying sick persons to him; others were pushing the sick aside.

Using all his remaining strength, the shepherd elbowed his way through the crowd until he was close to Jesus. He felt the healer's loving eyes on him. There was the touch of Jesus' strong hand and a word in his low voice. The shepherd's pain grew less. His strength came back. He knew that he had been made well again.

Gratefully the shepherd reached into his moneybag for the thirty gilt pennies. He tried to empty them into the hands that had healed him.

But Jesus said, "I need no silver or gold. If you wish to show gratitude, you may take your money to the temple. There it will be used for the needs of the people."

The shepherd hurried to the temple and found the box for offerings. It would have been pleasant to drop the thirty shining coins, one by one. Their clink would have been cheery and musical as they joined the other money in the box. But something seemed to warn the shepherd to keep the coins wrapped together in the piece of cloth in which he had found them by the roadside thirty years ago. He dropped them, still wrapped in the protective cloth, into the offering box in the temple.

Judas Iscariot, a disciple of Jesus, had been hoping Jesus would be a strong earthly king. He had wanted Jesus to lead an army against the Romans to free the Jews. This week had seemed the perfect chance for Jesus to become the fighting leader of a revolution against the Romans. The city was full of Jews who had come there from all parts of the Meriterranean world for the Feast of the Passover. With Jesus as leader, thought Judas, the mobs could have driven out the Roman soldiers and put Jesus on the king's throne.

But now it seemed plain to Judas that Jesus cared only for helping people and telling them of God's great love for all. It was clear to him at last that Jesus had no thought of starting a riot to overthrow the Romans.

Judas had another idea. Perhaps he could put Jesus in a tight spot that would force him to fight. Perhaps Judas could fix it so that one of Jesus' enemies would attack him and make him stand up as a fighting leader of those who admired and followed him.

Judas knew that the chief priests in the temple were irked by Jesus' words and his charm that drew people to him. Judas would try to make a bargain with the priests.

"Would you like to capture Jesus of Nazareth?" Judas asked the chief priests.

The priests crowded about him. "Do you have a plan?"

"What will you give me if I deliver Jesus to you?"

One of the priests went to the temple treasury and examined its gold, silver, and copper. A little bag containing thirty gilt pennies seemed a handy reward to offer Judas.

Judas accepted the thirty gilt pennies and told the chief priests when to send the soldiers to look for Jesus on the Mount of Olives. To be sure they would have the right man arrested, Judas said, "The one I greet with a kiss will be the one to take."

Jesus was on the Mount of Olives at the time Judas had mentioned to the chief priests. While Roman soldiers watched, Judas greeted Jesus with a kiss. The man who had once been Judas' best friend was led away, a prisoner.

The next few hours were terrible ones for Judas. His hope that Jesus would be forced to lead a riot quickly disappeared. Then horror overwhelmed Judas. What had he done? Suppose Jesus still refused to use his powers to free himself from the soldiers? What had he done to the man he had followed as a friend?

Judas hurried to the temple. "Take back your money," he told the chief priests. "I was wrong. Jesus is innocent. Take back your money and free him!"

The priests shrugged their shoulders. "What is that to us? See to it yourself."

Judas pleaded. The chief priests were firm. Judas looked at the coins in his hand. What had he done! Traded the life of a good man for these! Judas flung the thirty gilt pennies to the floor. Too ashamed of himself to wish to live another day, he went out, alone, and he hanged himself.

When Judas had gone, the chief priests picked up the coins from the floor. "It would not be right," said one, "to put these back in the temple treasury."

"No," said another. "No, indeed. They are 'blood money.' They do not belong in the temple treasury."

"We need a field to use as a burial place for strangers and for the poor who cannot afford a place," suggested one priest. "I know of a field for sale—the field of a potter."

"Good," the priests agreed. "That is a suitable suggestion."

So some of the thirty gilt pennies bought the potter's field as a grave-yard for strangers and for the poor. There were enough left over to pay the soldiers who guarded the tomb where the body of Jesus was laid after his death on the cross.

The coins, tainted by Judas' deception and separated each from the others, had lost their value. The thirty gilt pennies were no longer a treasure.

Where Legend Touches the Bible Story

Terah and Abraham move from Ur

Genesis 11:26-31; 12:1-9

Abraham buys land from the Hittites in Canaan

Genesis 23:1-20

Joseph is sold to the Ishmaelites

Genesis 37:3-36

Jacob's sons buy grain from Egypt

Genesis 42–47:1-12

Death and burial of Jacob

Genesis 49:28-33; 50:1-14

The queen of Sheba brings gold to King Solomon in Jerusalem

I Kings 10:1-13

The temple treasury is robbed and contents carried to the East

II Kings 24:5-17

Three kings from the East bring gifts to the Christ child

Matthew 2:1-12

Mary and Joseph flee with the Christ child to Egypt

Matthew 2:13-15

Jesus heals the sick in the temple

Matthew 21:9-14

Coins from the temple treasury pay Judas

Matthew 26:14-50

Judas' money, thrown to the ground, buys a burial field

Matthew 27:1-10, 65-66

DATE DUE

JUL 7 1982		
OCT 24		
OCT 2 6		
FEB 1 7		
MAY 02		
FEB 2 1		
Gomez		
OCT 24		
MAY 1 1		

HIGHSMITH 45-102   PRINTED IN U.S.A.